KU-556-882

Long ago, John Lambton went fishing on a Sunday. The villagers were shocked.

'Tut tut! Fishing?' they said. 'That boy should not be out having fun on a Sunday!'

John was the son of a lord. He thought he could do as he pleased. So he sat by the River Wear and fished.

After two hours, he had caught
nothing. He was about to pack up and go.
Suddenly he felt a sharp tug on his line.

He had caught something! He tried
to pull it in, but it fought hard.
It must be a huge fish! thought John.

At last, he dragged it onto the bank.
But it was not a fish. It was a slimy black
worm with an ugly head. It was small but
scary ... and very smelly!

7

It wriggled and snapped at John. Its teeth were as sharp as needles.

John did not like the look of it at all.

He was about to throw it back in the river.
Just then, a strange old man appeared.

'Keep it, or you will be sorry, lad!' said the
old man. Then he vanished into thin air.

There is something fishy going on, thought John. He put the worm in his fishing basket.

But it looked so evil he was afraid to keep it. So he threw it down the village well.

John went home to Lambton Hall.

'Did you catch any fish?' asked
Lord Lambton.

'No, Father,' said John.
He did not dare tell him
about the worm.

Years went by and nothing terrible happened. John grew up and went off to war. He forgot all about the worm.

But the worm did not forget about him. It was still in the well. It grew and grew.

Soon, it had grown into a giant serpent.
One night, it slithered out of the well.
It went back to the river and
wrapped itself around the island.

The next day the worm made
its way to Lambton Hall.

'Let's feed it before it kills us all!'
said the villagers.

They gave it a trough of milk.
The worm drank the lot and left. It
wrapped itself around Penshaw Hill
and slept.

But every day, the worm came back.
It wanted more. The villagers fed it milk
and cows and sheep. They knew it would
kill them if they did not.

Every night, it went back to Penshaw
Hill to sleep. The villagers lived in fear.

After seven years, John came back from war. On his way home, he met a wise woman.

'John Lambton, you put the worm in the well,' she said. 'So you are the only one who can kill it.'

John went pale. How did she know his secret?

'How can I kill the worm?' he asked.

'Tell the blacksmith to make you a suit of spiky armour,' she said. 'When the worm wraps itself around you, the spikes will stab it.'

'I will go to the blacksmith now,' said John.

'Wait!' said the wise woman. 'There is more! After you kill the worm, return to Lambton Hall. You must kill the first thing you see when you arrive. If you do not, the Lambton family will have nothing but bad luck.'

When the armour was ready, John put it on.

'Father, I am going to kill the worm,' he said. 'Afterwards, I will blow my horn and you must send the dog to greet me.'

'Why?' asked Lord Lambton.

'I must kill the first thing I meet on my return. If I don't, we will be cursed,' said John.

19

That night, he rode to Penshaw Hill.
The worm was wrapped around it.
    John crept up. Suddenly, it grabbed
him! It wrapped him in its giant coils.

John gasped for breath. The worm
squeezed him tighter and tighter.

But as it squeezed, the spikes
on the armour stabbed it.

STAB!

STAB!

STAB!

At last, the worm
was dead!

John rode back to Lambton Hall and blew his horn. But the dog did not run out to greet him.

Instead Lord Lambton rushed to greet his son. John could not kill his father!

Just then, the dog ran out too and John killed it instead.

Alas, he had not done as the wise woman said.

After that, the Lambtons had nothing
but bad luck. Everyone said that they
were cursed.

And all because John Lambton went
fishing on a Sunday!

THE
LAMBTON WORM

Retold by Jeanne Willis
Series Advisor Professor Kimberley Reynolds
Illustrated by Pierre Kleinhouse

91120000403355

Letter from the Author

I love writing stories about animals, monsters and aliens. I have also written books about my pet rabbit, rat, toad, cat and Betty, my snake. But I have never written one about a worm until now.

The Lambton Worm was a monster who lived in the north of England long ago. The legend says that it was so big, it curled itself right round Penshaw Hill. If you visit the hill today, some folk say you can still see the marks of its coils. Did the Lambton Worm really exist?

BRENT LIBRARIES	
WIL	
91120000403355	
Askews & Holts	08-May-2019
JF	£7.75